Until You
Came Along

Book Design by *the*BookDesigners

Printed in China

ISBN: 978-0-578-70028-1

www.untilyoucamealong.com

Until You Came Along

BRENDAN CASEY

ILLUSTRATED BY
CASEY WHITE

You don't know this. And, why should you? You're young. Like life altering - sleep stealing – are you even still breathing - your mom's chest is your dinner plate - kind of young. You're a formless glob of soft, carefully powdered skin and the tiniest of bones. You've got a head you can't even hold up yet. You nap, you eat, you crap, you cry.

So, what I'm about to tell you won't make sense. You won't comprehend it now, or, for that matter, years to come. But your parents were once real people. They had lives all their own. They had goals, both personal and professional. They enjoyed things like – well, fun! Specifically, wine and yoga and concerts and weekends.

They traveled. Hawaii, Thailand, Italy, the Caribbean. It was peaceful and fun and educational. They had hobbies. Like hiking. And cooking. Pick-up basketball on Saturday. Company softball on Tuesday.

And speaking of companies, they had jobs. They still do, of course. But back then they were driven. They had careers they valued. They wore grown-up clothes from grown-up stores because they were vain and Target wasn't on their radar yet. They angled for promotions, begged for raises, and fudged their expenses.

They did Happy Hour.

Holy Hell! Remember Happy Hour? How good does that sound? Drink specials. Draft beers. Wings. Sliders. Bacon wrapped sliders. Bacon wrapped hotdogs. Bacon wrapped dates.

BACON WRAPPED FREEDOM TO DO WHATEVER THE HELL THEY WANTED BECAUSE YOU DIDN'T EXIST!

And Then You Came Along.

And you turned two very nice, well rounded people into parents. Dick move, pal. So, we dedicate this book to you, you carefully swaddled bandit of fun and excitement. You sucked the life out of life like so much formula through a rubber nipple.

Or so we thought.

Once upon a time, in the long-forgotten land of childless bliss, your parents were attractive. We primped and combed and obsessed. We moisturized and exfoliated. Mom was stunning. Dad was handsome.

Our clothes were trendy and expensive. Our shoes were sexy and impractical and hurt our feet. But it was worth it...

Like, so damn worth it.

We had cool hair. We used product, got color, and went to salons. We shaved and plucked and waxed. Every last follicle groomed perfect. It was painful and time consuming.

But, IT WAS WORTH IT.

We turned heads and got compliments.

UNTIL YOU CAME ALONG!

We used to work out. We went to the gym. We lifted. We "did cardio."

We trashed our delts, and thrashed our backs. We hit Bi's and Tri's. Our core was our everything. Spin class. Cross-fit. Cardio Barre. We were there. Leg day. Cheat day. Off day.

THAT WAS OUR WEEK.

Dad cut the sleeves off his tees. He bought cross-trainers. Mom owned sports bras. And yoga pants. And people noticed.

We had great butts, and flat stomachs, and the mirror to prove it. Our body was our temple. We were ripped. And beautiful. And toned.

WE LOOKED GOOD NAKED.

UNTIL YOU CAME ALONG!

Your mom and dad had sex. On the reg. We boned. We banged. We balled. We shagged. And it was hot. It was fun. It was dirty.

There were outfits and candles. Oils to last longer. Gels to finish harder. AND!

POSITION CHANGES.

Dorsal. Doggy. Cowgirl. The Oven Mitt.

Sweet Mother of Mary we moved around.

A LOT!

The lights were on, the clothes were off, and we did it all. It was athletic and fun and pleasurable.

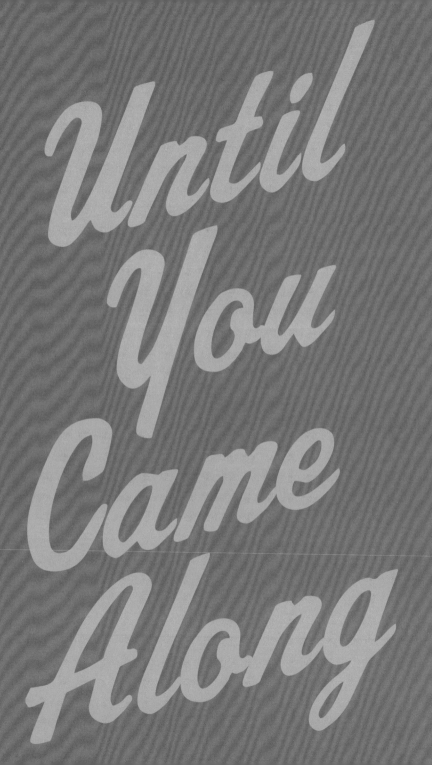

Until You Came Along

Your parents loved food. Like real food. Not stuff prepared in a microwave, passed through a fast food window, or foraged from betwixt the seats of our car.

We did brunch. That gloriously lazy, alcohol-fueled hybrid of lunch and breakfast. That boozy mid-day feast made popular by baby showers and unemployed hipsters.

We paired omelets with Prosecco and chased bacon with beer. We used words like "tartine" and "frittata." We divvied up small bites, slurped oysters, and pounded pancakes.

The food was decadent. The mimosas, bottomless.

It was the highlight of our weekend.

Until You Came Along!

*W*e did Taco Tuesday. A whole day dedicated to one delicious delicacy from south of the border. Shredded beef, cheese, lettuce, and friends.

ON A TUESDAY!

We fancied Food Trucks. Curbside Korean BBQ and Lobster Rolls in Loading Zones. Fried Chicken and Southern Style fries...

...with a whiff of exhaust fumes and a hint of brake dust.

We ate at actual restaurants. Places with booths and bars and tablecloths!

We made reservations, ordered apps, and agonized over the dessert menu.

UNTIL YOU CAME ALONG!

*T*he office is empty and your parents are tipsy. It's Happy Hour. That magical time when booze beckoned and work waited.

We chugged lagers and sipped Manhattans. We high fived and gossiped and played trivia. We longed for raises, poked fun at our bosses, and tossed back shots.

We paid the price the next morning.

Bartenders became friends. Co-workers, confidants.

The drinks were half-priced. The stress rum soaked and tomorrow's problem.

UNTIL YOU CAME ALONG!

We were season ticket holders. Section 12. Row 23. Seat 15. And for six Saturdays every fall we went back to school...

FOR FOOTBALL.

We grilled meats, wore tank-tops, and sang the fight song—loudly, and off-key.

We drank beer from funnels and bourbon from the bottle. We shot Fireball, downed Jaeger and inhaled cholesterol.

We used words like tradition. And scheme. And half-time adjustments. We sat with people named Frosty Ron, Dirty Laundry and The Bump. We chanted. And taunted. And cried.

And cheered our fucking hearts out.

We loved our team. We loved each other. We were family.

Until You Came Along

We drove nice cars. They were gaudy and sleek and European.

Immaculate chrome. Perfect tires.

They ran on gas. Because fuck the sun.

It was horsepower and leather and speeding tickets and crazy insurance rates.

BUT WE DIDN'T CARE.

They were our FIRST babies. An extension of us. A symbol of our rise through the ranks. We worked. We achieved. We saved.

AND IT FELT GOOD.

They turned heads. Roared. And monitored blind spots. We named them Thor and Paulina.

And we went everywhere together.

UNTIL YOU CAME ALONG!

*W*e watched TV. A lot. Comedy. Drama. Reality. We devoured it all.

We binged. We Netflixed. We Primed.

We kept up with the Kardashians and Flipped That House. We cheered for chefs, voted off Idols, and cackled at Bachelorettes. We solved crime, pined for dragons and obsessed over docs.

We lost remotes, paused games, had a Dish, and even snuck glances at work.

Dateline was our Date Night.

TV was our sanctuary. A 4K HD portal to relaxation. An escape from adulthood. Just us and the screen and our stories...

...And the wine. And the popcorn. And the couch. God, we were close.

TV was safe. It was comforting. It was oh-so-wonderfully mindless.

UNTIL YOU CAME ALONG!

Mom did spa days.

Entire afternoons devoted to pampered relaxation. High priced, robe clad maintenance for the body and mind.

Hours of deep tissue healing. Swedish rub downs and apricot exfoliating scrub.

There were masks of clay, baths of mud and complimentary champagne.

There was mineral water, exotic teas, and ...

COMPLIMENTARY CHAMPAGNE!

The Jacuzzi bubbled and the sauna beckoned. The halls were fragrant, the oils essential.

It was a candle laden, lavender-scented haven of self-care.

Until You Came Along!

*D*ad played fantasy sports.

He hosted drafts, proposed trades and lived on the waiver wire. He studied and did research. He went full numbers-nerd.

Games became matchups. Players reduced to stats. OPS. ERA. QBR. WHIP.

He flunked calculus, but understood sabermetrics. Moneyball made sense. Credit cards didn't.

He berated friends, trash-talked co-workers, and cried over injuries. He took it way too seriously. It was competitive and intense.

It was all fucking make believe...

*A*nd now we play hide and seek. We play peek-a-boo. We wear tiaras, and fire helmets, and capes. Sometimes Dad's a prince. Sometimes Mom's a fairy. Other days we're frogs.

Because... we're being frogs and that's cool.

We do anything for laughs.

Tea parties with stuffed bears. Trips to the moon with a plush duck. We dance and sing and kiss your toys goodnight.

We build forts, (block AND pillow). We slide and swing and make shit out of sand.

We race cars and crash trucks. We collect dolls and put on make-up.

We pretend. We imagine. We dream.

It's ALL make-believe. And we never want it to end.

*Y*ou came along and now we own a mini-van. It's clunky and generic. It's boring and roomy.

It's fucking white.

But it's safe. It's responsible. It's adulthood on wheels. Maturity with a lift gate and a fold away third row. It doesn't turn heads, or do the zero to sixty thing.

It just protects.

YOU.

It plays DVD's and swallows your toys. It's my Batmobile and you're my Robin. My diaper clad partner in crime. Now, we go everywhere together.

And I wouldn't have it any other way.

Our lives aren't craft beer and freedom anymore. It's not all day shopping sprees, afternoons by the pool, or weekly trips to the nail salon.

It's simple. And pure. And happy.

It's paint. And coloring books. And play-doh. Damn, we missed play-doh.

We laugh at silly stuff. Like burps and cartoons and the dog.

We blow bubbles like it's a science. We make paper airplanes like it's art. You love the hose and the vacuum cleaner, and we can't figure out why.

We don't do yoga anymore. Or spin. Or lift.

We just carry.

We carry you up the stairs. We carry you to the car. We carry you to bed. Our cores are crap. They're all love and no abs.

And we don't give a shit.

We're not cross-fitters. Or Mimosa drinkers. We're not scratch golfers, die-hard fans, or night owls.

WE'RE PARENTS, GODDAMN IT.

We go to bed at nine. And wake up at one. And again at four.

And sometimes at six.

We complain to our friends, but deep down we love it. Because it means more time with you.

And Until You Came Along, we had no idea just how hard we could love. So, bring on the diapers. Strap me into that mini-van. And get me to the playground.

BECAUSE YOU DID COME ALONG.

AND YOU CHANGED EVERYTHING.

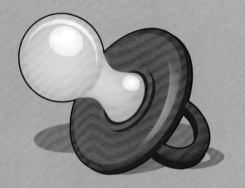